GOD'S MISSIONARY
The Faith of Thomas

Written by The Voice of the Martyrs
with Cheryl Odden
Illustrated by G. R. Erlan

The Voice of the Martyrs is a Christian nonprofit ministry dedicated to serving Christians who are persecuted for their faith. The ministry helps Christians living in nations hostile to the gospel, including communist and Islamic countries. Founded in 1967 by Richard and Sabina Wurmbrand, a Romanian couple once imprisoned for their faith, The Voice of the Martyrs has a network of offices around the globe dedicated to helping the persecuted church. The ministry fulfills the Wurmbrands' vision to raise awareness about the plight of the persecuted church and to assist those suffering for their Christian witness.

To receive a free newsletter and learn how you can help today's persecuted church, contact:

The Voice of the Martyrs
PO Box 443
Bartlesville, OK 74005
(800) 747-0085
E-mail: thevoice@vom-usa.org
Website:
www.persecution.com
Youth website:
www.kidsofcourage.com

For today's apostles in India who suffer
for their faith in Jesus Christ.

A Note from the Director

O f all the stories about the apostles who were martyred for their Christian witness, Thomas' is perhaps the most talked about. In fact, more has been written about Thomas' apostleship to India in songs, poems and stories than is written about his discipleship in the Gospels. Christians in India still celebrate his arrival with the gospel and his martyrdom in their country.

Born in Galilee, Thomas was among the original 12 disciples called by Jesus. His career remains a mystery, but some have assumed he was a fisherman (John 21). Of the references to Thomas in the Gospels, his words are recorded only in the Book of John.

When the disciples object to Jesus going to Judea where Lazarus has died, Thomas' first recorded words are, "Let us all go that we may die with Him." The disciples knew the last time they were in Judea the Jews threatened to stone Jesus. Yet a willing Thomas courageously rallies the troops. They go to Judea, and Jesus raises Lazarus from the dead. The whole point of this miracle is to glorify God. Jews and Jesus' disciples witness a resurrection, solidifying belief that Jesus is God's son. Jesus then takes the opportunity to share one of his eight "I am" statements: "I am the resurrection and the life." But in the end, it takes a brash statement and dramatic demonstration to get Thomas to believe.

During the Last Supper, Jesus makes yet another plea to the disciples to believe in him. After Jesus tells them he will prepare a place for them, Thomas unabashedly asks, "Lord, we do not know where you are going, and how can we know the way?" Perhaps he still had not grasped the spiritual kingdom of Jesus Christ. Perhaps, still grappling with the reality of a physical kingdom, Thomas thought Jesus was going to some glorious physical city where he would then reign. Jesus responds with another "I am" statement: "I am the way, the truth and the life. No one comes to the Father except through Me." Once again, Jesus tells them that if they have seen Jesus, they have seen the Father.

Thomas' final exchanges are found in the concluding chapters of John, after Christ's death and resurrection. Thomas stares in disbelief when several disciples tell him about Jesus' after-death appearance to them. "Unless I see in His hands the print of the nails, and put my finger into the print of the nails, and put my hand into His side, I will not believe," demands Thomas. Because of these words, he has been called "Doubting Thomas."

But days later, Thomas is with the disciples when Jesus appears again. Jesus looks right at Thomas and challenges the skeptic: "Reach your finger here, and look at My hands; and reach your hand here, and put it into My side. Do not be unbelieving, but believing."

Immediately, Thomas cries out, "My Lord and my God!"

Jesus ascended into heaven, and from what history tells us the apostles soon divided the known world among themselves to evangelize. According to one account, for Thomas the lot fell to India, along with Ethiopia and Parthia (in modern-day Iran). At that time, "Ethiopia" included Africa (as we know it today) and parts of Persia. But it was in India that Thomas was martyred. There are several traditions recounting Thomas' mission in India.

In the Indian tradition, which has been passed down orally through the centuries, Thomas arrived around A.D. 50 or 52 on India's Malabar Coast (west) in the state of Cochin, which is a major spice exporting port even today. He founded seven churches, usually named as Crangamore, Quilon, Paravur, Kokkamangalam, Niranam, Palayur and Cayal. Thousands turned to Christ through his ministry, with one source claiming these specific numbers of conversions from the different levels of Hindu's caste system: 6,850 Brahmin, 2,590 Kshatriyas, and 3,780 Vaishyas, in addition to two kings and seven village chiefs. This story claims that Thomas preached east and west on the subcontinent, and one tradition suggests he even went to China.

According to Indian tradition, Thomas was martyred at the hands of Brahmin priests who were performing a ritual. Thomas challenged them and won, but he was then killed by the priests. His martyrdom is believed to have occurred around A.D. 70. This is the story the author will tell on the following pages.

Today in India, there is a group of Christians who trace their origins to the apostle Thomas. Called "St. Thomas Christians," they have used songs and poetry to maintain this tradition through the centuries.

St. Thomas' grave is on a hill called St. Thomas Mount at Mylapore, which is where he is believed to have been martyred. Over the centuries, artifacts have been discovered to provide evidence of the apostle's adventures and martyrdom on the mostly Hindu subcontinent. And liturgies in the Near East's ancient churches have given St. Thomas credit for being India's first apostle, pointing those in India to the same Jesus who told Thomas, "I am the way, the truth and the life."

As your children read about this doubter turned faith-filled missionary, it is my prayer that they will be inspired by Thomas' trust in God. And may the story encourage and lead them on their own faith adventure to share the gospel with their friends.

Dr. Tom White
Executive Director
The Voice of the Martyrs (USA)

"**L**et's go back to Judea and see Lazarus," said Jesus. Lazarus was very sick, and the time was right for a miracle, to show that he was the Son of God.

"But Master," said one, "the Jews in Judea want to kill you. We don't stand a chance."

One disciple was not afraid. His name was Thomas. He stood up and said, "Let's all go and die with him!"

3

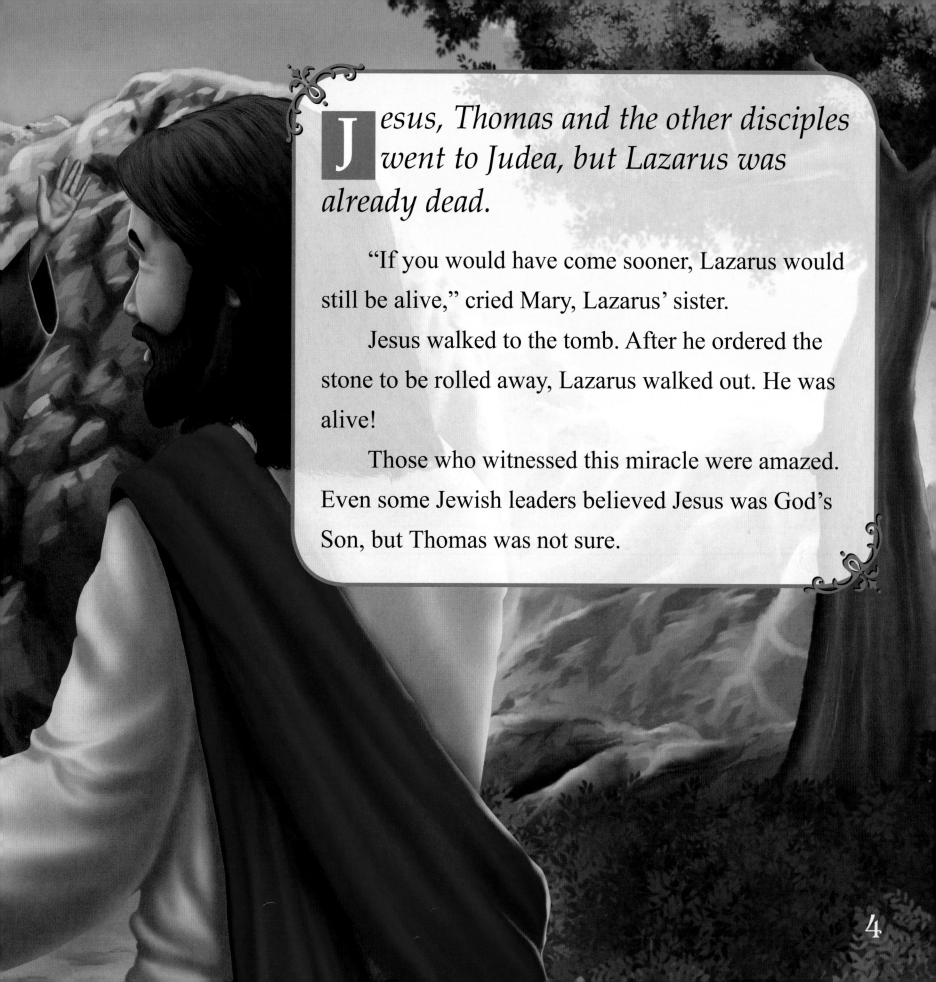

Jesus, Thomas and the other disciples went to Judea, but Lazarus was already dead.

"If you would have come sooner, Lazarus would still be alive," cried Mary, Lazarus' sister.

Jesus walked to the tomb. After he ordered the stone to be rolled away, Lazarus walked out. He was alive!

Those who witnessed this miracle were amazed. Even some Jewish leaders believed Jesus was God's Son, but Thomas was not sure.

One evening as Jesus ate dinner with Thomas and the other disciples, he told them that he was going to die on the cross.

"Don't worry," said Jesus, comforting his disciples who were saddened by the news. "You trust God, don't you? Now you need to trust me. You know where I am going and how to get there."

"We do not know where you are going," said Thomas, confused. "How do we get there?"

Jesus looked into Thomas' bewildered face and said, "I am the way, the truth, and the life. No one comes to the Father except through me."

6

The day came when Jewish leaders and soldiers arrested Jesus. He was tried and nailed to a cross. But the people's hatred did not end with Jesus' death. Many of his followers were also hated. Thomas and the other disciples were afraid, knowing they, too, could be killed. So they hid.

9

ang! The disciples burst through the door. "Thomas!" they shouted, unable to contain their excitement. "We saw Jesus. He's alive!"

Thomas shook his head in disbelief. *Impossible!* thought Thomas as his eyes narrowed into a scowl. *He's gone forever.*

"I don't believe you," he snapped.

"But Thomas, we saw him!" they repeated.

"I'll only believe it if I see the holes from the nails and put my fingers into them."

Eight days later the disciples were hiding in a locked room. Jewish leaders still roamed the streets hunting down anyone claiming to follow Jesus. Suddenly, Jesus appeared to them.

"Put your finger here in my hands," Jesus said, looking right at Thomas. "Don't be a doubter. Believe!"

"My Lord and my God!" cried Thomas. Seeing Jesus' scars was the proof he needed.

"You believe because you just saw me," said Jesus. "Blessed are those who have not seen and yet believe."

Later, Thomas would give his life for those who had not seen Jesus and yet believed.

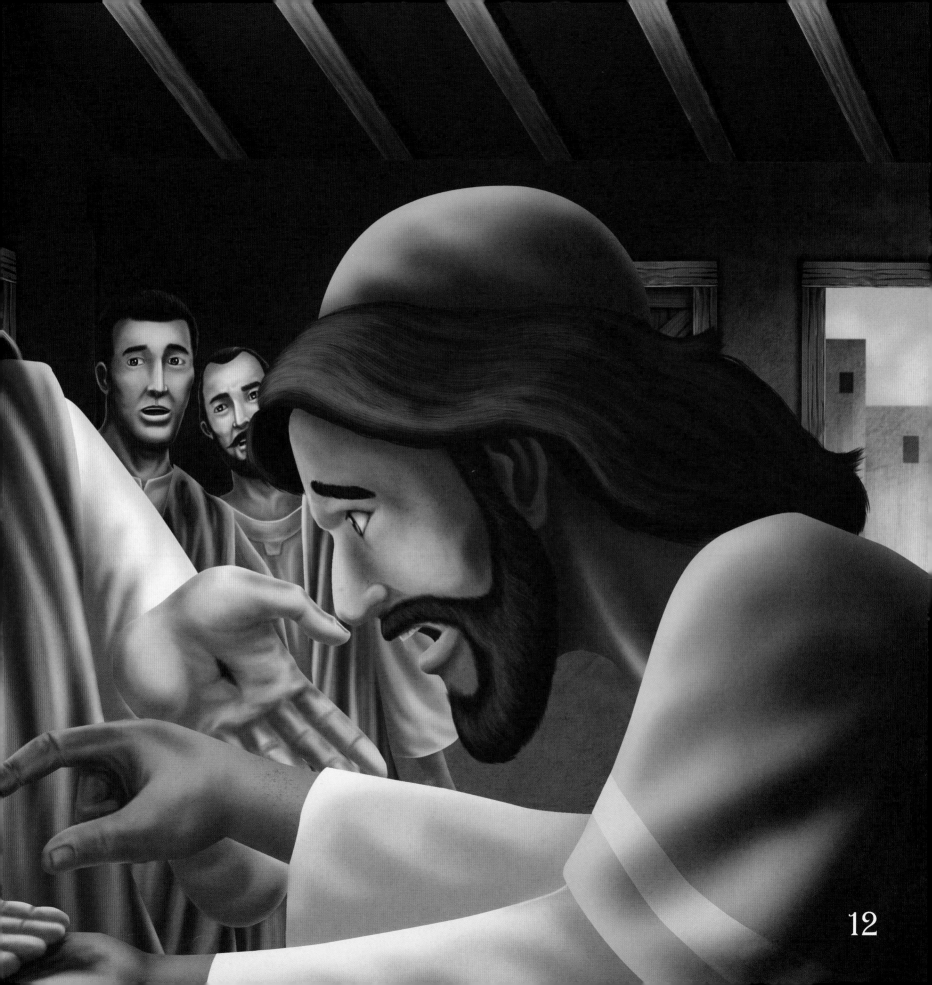

12

13

Thomas and the other 10 disciples gathered on a mountain in Galilee.

Jesus appeared to them and gave them his final instructions before he returned to heaven.

"Go and make followers of me in all nations," he told them.

14

The day finally came when Thomas walked through the gates of Jerusalem, carrying with him only what he needed.

Like the other apostles, he started his journey to spread the gospel to the ends of the earth. His travels would take him to a strange and exotic place.

17

Before Thomas arrived in India, he traveled through Persia (called Iran today), where many had not yet heard about Jesus.

Thomas preached about Jesus Christ and his free gift of eternal life. Many placed their trust in Jesus.

Soon Thomas knew his time in Persia was done, so he boarded a ship and left for India.

PERSIA

PERSIAN GULF

19

21

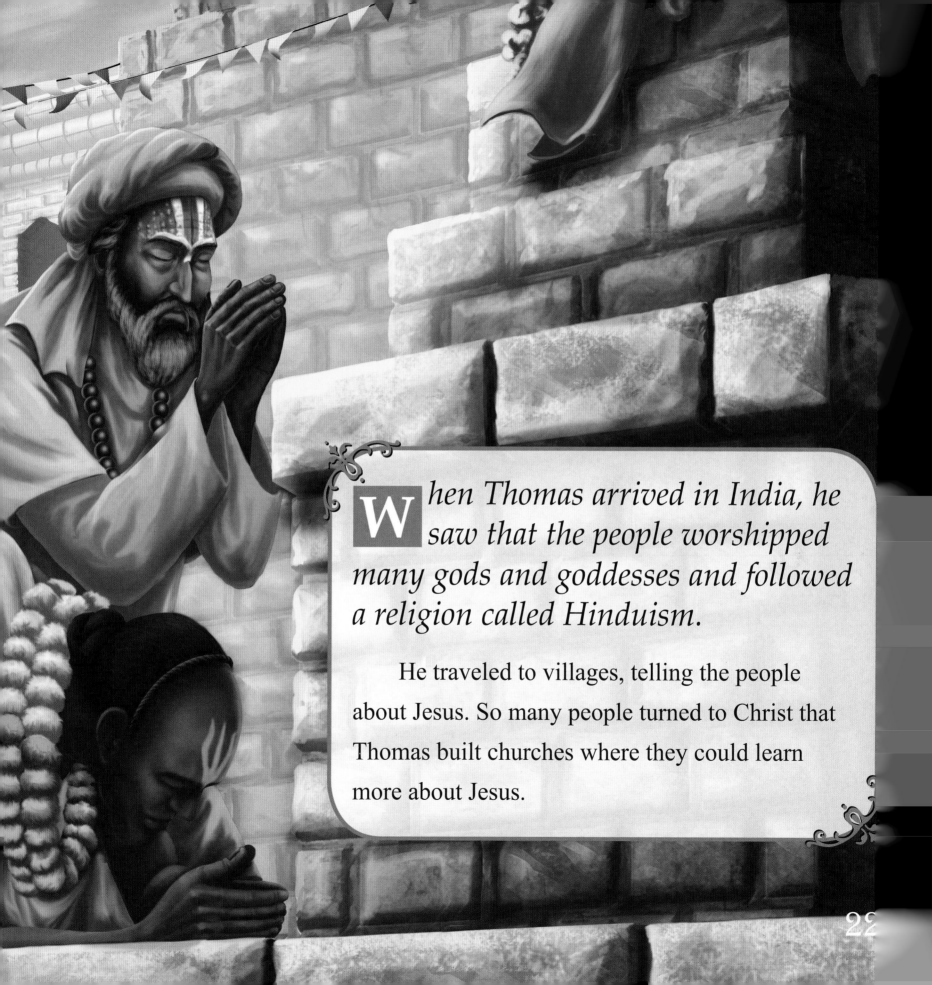

When Thomas arrived in India, he saw that the people worshipped many gods and goddesses and followed a religion called Hinduism.

He traveled to villages, telling the people about Jesus. So many people turned to Christ that Thomas built churches where they could learn more about Jesus.

When the people turned to Christ, they left their false gods and goddesses and burned their Hindu temples.

Some Hindus were furious with Thomas for turning people away from their religion, which began in their country long before Jesus was born. Soon Thomas would face their anger, and it would cost him his life.

24

One day, Thomas met a group of Hindu priests whose actions puzzled him. They were tossing water into the air while chanting their prayers.

"Why are you doing that?" asked Thomas.

"The water is our sacrifice to the gods," they replied.

"Then why aren't your gods accepting it?" asked Thomas, who watched as the water droplets kept returning to the ground.

26

Surely the priests thought this strange looking man was crazy.

"Who can make the water hang in the air?" mocked the priests.

"I can," claimed Thomas.

"Then prove it!" they said.

28

Thomas' face brightened as he saw his chance to tell them about Jesus.

"I will prove it to you," he replied. "But only if you promise to believe in God's Son and be baptized if I succeed."

The priests agreed to the deal. How could they lose? They would prove Thomas wrong.

30

Thomas walked up to the basin, cupped the cool water in his hands, and tossed it up into the air.

The priests looked up into the blue sky, waiting for the drops to fall to the ground. But they didn't. Some say the water drops hung in the air and sparkled like diamonds!

Thomas looked at the priests, whose faces darkened with anger.

"Worship the goddess!" demanded one who refused to be proven wrong.

"I worship the one true God and his Son, Jesus," replied Thomas. "I cannot worship your gods."

The priests knew Thomas' God was real, and that made them mad. So they put an end to this gospel preacher for good. A priest grabbed a spear and threw it, piercing Thomas' side.

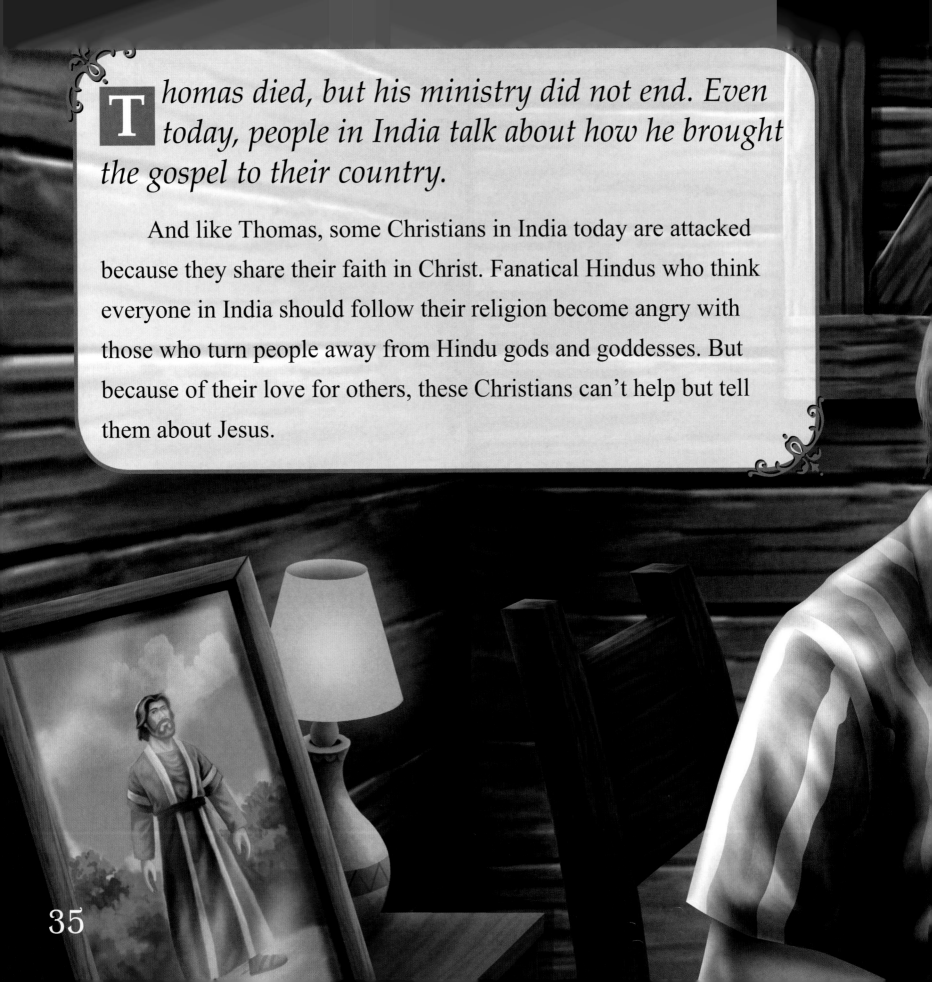

homas died, but his ministry did not end. Even today, people in India talk about how he brought the gospel to their country.

And like Thomas, some Christians in India today are attacked because they share their faith in Christ. Fanatical Hindus who think everyone in India should follow their religion become angry with those who turn people away from Hindu gods and goddesses. But because of their love for others, these Christians can't help but tell them about Jesus.

37

When you tell a friend about Jesus, remember: God promises to give you that same faith and courage that he gave to Thomas in India. All you have to do is ask, and the next step is yours!

38

For Reflection

"I was with you in weakness, in fear, and in much trembling. And my speech and my preaching were not with persuasive words of human wisdom, but in demonstration of the Spirit and of power, that your faith should not be in the wisdom of men but in the power of God."

—1 Corinthians 2:3–5

What does it mean to have faith in Jesus?

Before Jesus died on the cross, did Thomas believe that Jesus was the Son of God?
How about after Jesus died on the cross?

What does it mean to have a strong faith in Jesus? Why was it important for Thomas to have a strong faith in Jesus before he went to Persia and then India?

Do you think Thomas felt scared when he challenged the priests in India?

When you tell a friend about Jesus, do you feel scared?

Read 1 Corinthians 2:3–5.
What does God promise to do when we tell others about Jesus even when we're scared?

Prayer

Dear Jesus,

Thank you for the example of Thomas, who once doubted you but later became strong in faith and took the gospel to India. When I share about you with my friends, please give me the power that you promise, even if I feel scared. I pray for Christians in India who are opposed because they tell others about you. I pray that you will also strengthen their faith. In Jesus' name,

Amen.

Bibliography

Foxe, John and The Voice of the Martyrs. *Foxe: Voices of the Martyrs* (Orlando, FL: Bridge-Logos, 2007).

Holman QuickSource Bible Atlas (Nashville, TN: Holman Bible Publishers, 2005).

Huc, M. L'Abbé. *Christianity in China, Tartary, and Thibet, Volume I* (London: Longman, Brown, Green, Longmans, & Roberts, 1857).

Moffett, Samuel Hugh. *A History of Christianity in Asia, Volume I: Beginnings to 1500* (Maryknoll, NY: Orbis Books, 1998).

Neill, Stephen. *A History of Christianity in India: The Beginnings to AD 1707* (New York: Cambridge University Press, 1984).

Van Braght, Thieleman J. *Martyrs Mirror* (Scottdale, PA: Herald Press, 1994).

The following Bible versions were consulted in the writing of the story:

Look for these other great story books from Living Sacrifice Book Company, publishing division of The Voice of the Martyrs.

Holiday Heroes

The Story of St. Patrick:
More than Shamrocks and Leprechauns

The Story of St. Nicholas:
More than Reindeer and a Red Suit

The Story of St. Valentine:
More than Cards and Candied Hearts

Christian Outlaws

God's Pilgrim: The Real Story of John Bunyan and *The Pilgrim's Progress*

God's Outlaw: The Real Story of William Tyndale and the English Bible

God's Prisoner:
The Story of Richard Wurmbrand

The Early Church

God's Apostle: The Adventures of Paul

God's Witness: The Courage of Stephen

Stories of Christian Heroes on DVD
For ages 8 to 12

The Jim Elliot Story

The John Bunyan Story

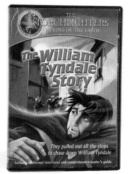

The William Tyndale Story

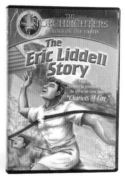

The Eric Liddell Story

The Gladys Aylward Story

The Perpetua Story

The Richard Wurmbrand Story

For more information on these and other available products,
go to www.vombooks.com or call (800) 747-0085.